THE X FILES™

FIGHT THE FUTURE

SCRAPBOOK

CREATED BY CHRIS CARTER

ADAPTED BY CAITLIN BLASDELL

Voyager

An Imprint of HarperCollins*Publishers*

HarperCollins*Publishers*
77–85 Fulham Palace Road,
Hammersmith, London W6 8JB

A Paperback Original 1998
9 8 7 6 5 4 3 2 1

A catalogue record for this book is available from the British Library

ISBN 0 00 648361 5

Printed and bound in Italy by Rotolito Lombarda

Cover artwork courtesy of and © 1998 Twentieth Century Fox Film Corporation

Interior design: Tanya Ross-Hughes, David Hughes/HOTFOOT Studio

Without warning a boy falls through the roof of the cave.

"Stevie? Hey, Stevie—are you okay?" his friends call from the opening above. The fall didn't hurt him. Slowly, Stevie gets to his feet. He spots some cool old human bones—and a skull.

But there is black oil under his sneaker and it's moving toward him—almost like it's ALIVE. Stevie's friends are worried about him. He doesn't answer their calls. As they stare down at him, Stevie's head falls backward. They can see his eyes turning completely, unnaturally black. They run for help.

One week later, in Dallas, Texas, a dozen FBI Agents hunt for a bomb. But Agent Fox Mulder thinks they're searching in the wrong place. He finds the bomb in the building across the street, hidden in a soda vending machine. But he's locked in!

He calls his partner and friend Agent Dana Scully on his cell phone. She gets everyone out of danger, including Mulder—just in time! The whole building **explodes** as the agents race away.

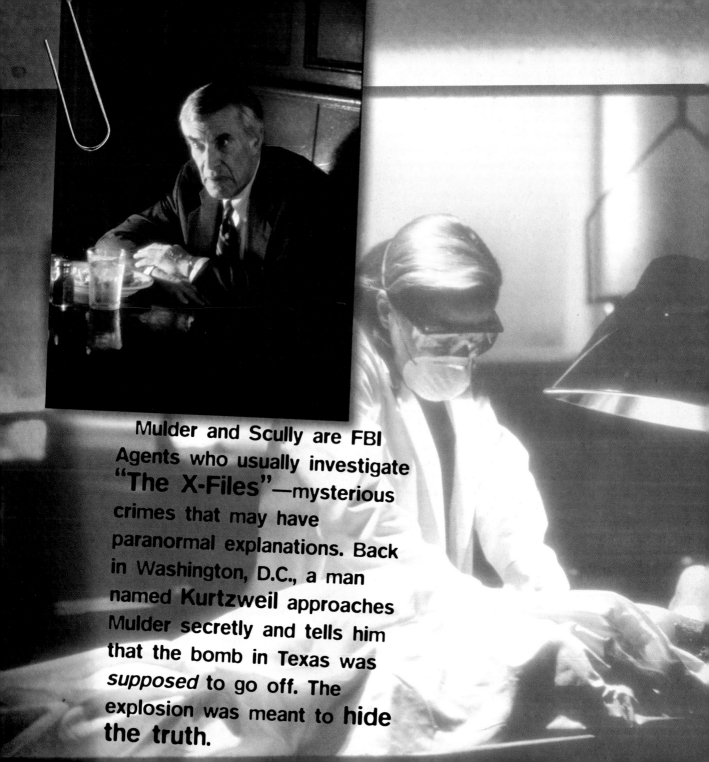

Mulder and Scully are FBI Agents who usually investigate "The X-Files"—mysterious crimes that may have paranormal explanations. Back in Washington, D.C., a man named Kurtzweil approaches Mulder secretly and tells him that the bomb in Texas was *supposed* to go off. The explosion was meant to hide the truth.

MULDER AND SCULLY HAVE TO INVESTIGATE THIS—ESPECIALLY SINCE THE **FBI** IS BLAMING **THEM** FOR THE EXPLOSION. THEY SNEAK INTO A HOSPITAL AND SCULLY DOES AN AUTOPSY ON THE BODY FOUND IN THE EXPLODED DALLAS BUILDING. THE BODY IS VERY STRANGE— SHE'S **NEVER** SEEN ANYTHING LIKE IT.

Meanwhile, back in Texas, strange things are happening at the cave. There are huge tanker trucks and helicopters everywhere. Inside the cave, doctors are studying a body. It's not alive, but it's not dead either—something weird is growing inside it. We can see a hand, an eye...it's an alien embryo.

The Cigarette-
Smoking Man, a
mysterious figure
linked to the
shadowy Syndicate,
wants to test a
vaccine on the
alien. One day when
the doctor enters
the cave, the body
is empty—

the alien

has escaped!

"Help!" the doctor calls. "I need help!"

A secret meeting is called by **the shadowy Syndicate**—a group of powerful men who have been working on a secret project for over fifty years. The **Cigarette-Smoking Man** and the **Well-Manicured Man** are there. The Syndicate is worried that Mulder and Scully will find out what they're doing in the Texas cave. **The FBI agents must be stopped.**

Meanwhile, Mulder and Scully have followed clues to the cave and found the right place but there is no cave! Only a suspiciously new park. Stevie's friends tell Mulder and Scully which way the mysterious tanker trucks went.

WHEN THEY EVENTUALLY FIND THE
TRUCKS, MULDER AND SCULLY SEE A
STRANGE SIGHT. A CORNFIELD IN THE
MIDDLE OF THE DESERT AND TWO
GLOWING WHITE DOMES. INSIDE
THE DOMES ARE ROWS OF WHAT LOOK
LIKE BOXES. THERE'S AN EERIE
HUMMING NOISE BUT MULDER AND
SCULLY DON'T KNOW WHERE IT'S
COMING FROM. MULDER HAS A BAD
FEELING ABOUT THIS PLACE.

"SCULLY, RUN!" THE BOXES OPEN AND THOUSANDS OF BEES SWARM OUT—**RIGHT AT THE AGENTS.** THEY ESCAPE OUTSIDE ONLY TO BE CHASED **BY HELICOPTERS** WITH BLINDING SEARCHLIGHTS. JUST AS MULDER AND SCULLY THINK THEY ARE TRAPPED, THE HELICOPTERS FLY AWAY.

Back in Washington, D.C., Mulder and Scully are in trouble with the FBI. THEY'VE BEEN INVESTIGATING EVEN THOUGH THEY WERE TOLD NOT TO. Their boss, Assistant Director Skinner, can't protect them. Nobody believes their accusation that the bomb in Texas was set off DELIBERATELY to hide incriminating EVIDENCE. No one wants to hear about their discoveries.

Scully comes to see Mulder at his apartment. She tells him she is resigning from the FBI.

"You can't quit, Scully," Mulder says. "I don't want to do this without you. I don't know if I can. And if I quit now, they win..." They look at each other solemnly and are about to kiss for the first time when Scully yells, "Ouch!" She's been stung by a bee that's been hiding in her jacket. She passes out and Mulder calls the paramedics. "What hospital are you taking her to?" Mulder asks them, worried about Scully. But the men aren't real paramedics. They shoot Mulder and drive away, kidnapping Scully.

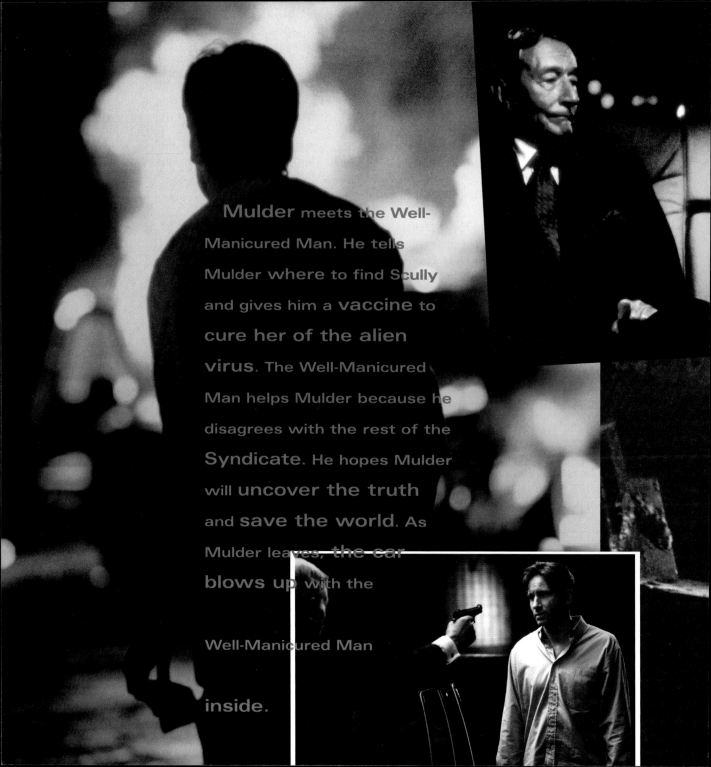

Mulder meets the Well-Manicured Man. He tells Mulder where to find Scully and gives him a **vaccine** to **cure her of the alien virus**. The Well-Manicured Man helps Mulder because he disagrees with the rest of the **Syndicate**. He hopes Mulder will **uncover the truth** and **save the world**. As Mulder leaves, the car **blows up** with the Well-Manicured Man inside.

Mulder goes to Antarctica. When he falls through a hole in the ice, he finds an enormous, alien spacecraft.

All of the icy corridors are lined with cryopods—
coffins holding aliens growing in people's frozen bodies.

Finally, Mulder finds Scully in a cryopod and injects her with the vaccine. The vaccine travels up the tube in her mouth and into the ship.

The vaccine works! The tube shrivels up. Scully wakes up but she is very cold and weak.

"Breathe, Scully, breathe!"
Mulder commands aloud.

IN THE MEANTIME, THE SHIP DETECTS THE VACCINE—IT STARTS TO SHAKE AND THE ICE MELTS EVERYWHERE. WORSE, THE ALIENS IN THE CRYOPODS ARE HATCHING. MULDER AND SCULLY HAVE TO GET OUT RIGHT AWAY. "SCULLY, CAN YOU WALK?"

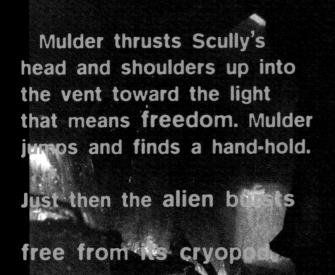

Mulder thrusts Scully's head and shoulders up into the vent toward the light that means **freedom**. Mulder jumps and finds a hand-hold.

Just then the alien bursts

free from its cryopod.

The creature grabs at Mulder's foot, its claws tearing at him. But as it stumbles from its pod, Mulder yanks himself from its grip and swings himself into the vent.

'Scully! Scully, we made it...'

Suddenly the ice they were standing on ripples and starts to give way, caving into the center of the buried ship. Mulder realizes what is happening. "We've got to run!" He drags Scully after him, struggling to outrace the collapsing ice but they can't run fast enough and they fall and fall and finally land hard. They land directly on the spaceship but then slide off onto the edge of the ice crater.

Ice chunks fall in a **terrible rain** all around them. Scully, still weak from the cryopod, lies face down in the snow. Above her, Mulder stares **awestruck** as the **ship lifts clear of the ice** and **disappears into the sky.** He's saved Scully but **once more** the evidence **to prove the truth** about the conspiracy had disappeared. **No one** will believe his story. But Mulder and Scully **keep trying** to do their best to **Fight the Future.**